Tamara Turtle's Life So Far

Written by Regan W. H. Macaulay
Illustrated by Javier Duarte

ISBN 978-1-61225-368-8

Published by Mirror Publishing
Milwaukee, WI 53214

Printed in the USA.

This book is dedicated to all the rescue organizations that care for and help Red-eared Sliders and turtles of all sorts find their forever homes.

A special thank you to Little RES Q for all their support and encouragement.

Thank you also to Devon, Jennifer, Marc, and Neil.

Tamara the turtle was a baby Red-eared Slider. She lived in a pet store, crammed into a tank with many other baby Red-eared Sliders.

The turtles scratched at the glass as customers passed,
and they dreamt of finding a home where they truly belonged.
Out of all the other turtles, a little boy and his mom
chose Tamara and took her to their house.

Tamara's new home was a clear tank filled halfway with water that sat in the corner on the little boy's desk. A dock was secured to one end. Tamara loved basking on her dock under a lightbulb and swimming in her water.

After a few months, the boy paid her less attention than he used to. He didn't change the water so often. He sometimes forgot to feed her. Tamara's shell started to feel funny, and she felt sick after swimming in her dirty water. Worst of all, the tank became too small for her!

The boy's mom came into the room one day. She looked sad. "Sorry, little turtle," she sighed. "I don't know what else to do."

The mom took Tamara and her tank outside to a creek that ran behind the house. She took off the lid and dumped Tamara into the creek and left her behind.

Tamara was alone and scared. She swam to shore and pulled her head into her shell. When the sun sank to the horizon, other turtles arrived. They were similar, but not the same as Tamara.

"What's she doing here?" asked one turtle. "She's a Red-eared Slider!"

Tamara poked her head out to speak. "What kind of turtle are you?"

"We are Painted turtles. We belong here."

Tamara's stomach churned from hunger and worry. "Why don't Red-eared Sliders belong here?"

Another Painted turtle replied in a gentler voice. "It's not your fault, dear," she said to Tamara. "When the wrong kind of animal is in the wrong place, it throws everything off. Painted turtles could disappear, and too many Red-eared Sliders would take their place."

Tamara had no desire to hurt anyone, so she decided to head out on her own to look for wherever she belonged. She made it to the edge of a sidewalk by nightfall. That was when her luck finally changed, and a human man noticed her.

"What on earth are you doing here?" asked the stranger. "Let's take you somewhere safe."

Tamara shrank back into her shell as the human picked her up.

Then they traveled in the stranger's car, while Tamara wondered where on earth she did belong.

"Here we are," said the man after driving for a while. "The Humane Society. You can stay at this shelter, and they will find you a good home."

Tamara spent many weeks getting to know the more unusual species at the Humane Society: one chinchilla, one parakeet, two iguanas, five hamsters, six rabbits, and seven rats.

There were also many, many turtles—all of them Red-eared Sliders, just like Tamara. She felt like she was back in the pet store, except she and the other turtles had much more room to swim.

Over time, she made new friends, her shell became stronger under the different kinds of lightbulbs, and her water never got dirty. Tamara grew to be a healthy, strong turtle.

Tamara's life so far had sometimes been unlucky, and she learned that most of the turtles at the shelter had similar pasts. Some of Tamara's new friends had been at the shelter for a year or more, but Tamara's life was about to get far luckier.

A woman arrived at the shelter and picked Tamara and her friend Apple to come home with her.

"I have a 500 gallon set-up with full-spectrum UV lighting and a basking lamp in my basement at home," the woman told one of the shelter workers. "I've got a big pond outside for the summer months. It is completely enclosed, so nothing can get in or out."

"Are these turtles for you, or are they a gift?" the shelter worker asked.

"They're for my whole family, but I will be the primary caretaker," the woman replied. "I'm a Herpetologist, and I've helped look after many turtles at my local zoo. I want my children to learn more about turtles, and I know exactly how to care for Red-eared Sliders."

Tamara turned to Apple with a big smile on her face. "That's where we belong!"

Tamara the turtle and her Red-eared Slider friend were going home.

Further information/resources:

Austin's Turtle Page care sheet for Red-eared Sliders:
http://www.austinsturtlepage.com/Care/caresheet-red_ear_slider.htm

Alberta Turtle and Tortoise Society:
https://www.facebook.com/AlbertaTurtleandTortoiseSociety/

California Turtle & Tortoise Club: http://tortoise.org/

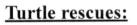

SC-C.A.R.E.S. (South Carolina): www.sc-cares.org

VA Reptile Rescue, Inc. (Virginia): www.vareptilerescue.org

Turtle rescues:

Arrowhead Reptile Rescue (Ohio): www.arrowheadreptilerescue.org

Forgotten Friend Reptile Sanctuary (Pennsylvania): http://forgottenfriend.org/

GNP Reptile Rescue (Peterborough, Ontario): reptilerescue.xp3.biz

International Reptile Rescue (Hart's Reptile World in Ohio):   http://www. hartsreptileworld.com/

Little RES Q (Markham, Ontario): http://littleresq.net/

Northeastern Reptile Welfare League (Vermont): http://www.nereptilewelfare.org/

R.S.P.C.A. Reptile Rescue UK: http://www.rspcareptilerescue.co.uk/

Reptile Rescue (Las Vegas, Nevada): www.reptilerescue.com

Reptile Rescue Center (Arkansas): http://www.reptilerescuecenter.org

Reptiles Rock! Reptile Education & Rescue Program
(Ottawa, Ontario): http://www.reptilesrock.ca/

Toronto Humane Society "Special Species" Department:
http://www.torontohumanesociety.com/adopt-a-pet/small-pets

Trancas Turtle and Koi Rescue (California): http://www.trancasturtlerescue.com/

Triple J Reptiles & Rescue (Pennsylvania): http://www.triplejreptilesandrescue.com/

Turtle Rescue of Long Island (New York):
www.turtlerescues.org

Turtle Rescue UK (Durham):
https://www.facebook.com/trukdurham/

Wichita Falls Reptile Rescue (Texas): http://www.facebook.com/reptilerescue

In Australia, the Red-Eared Slider is listed as a "pest species" and must, unfortunately, be euthanized if they are found. This is because they are not native to Australia and have the potential to breed quickly and take over the habitat of their native turtles. For more information regarding turtles and other reptiles in Australia, please visit Fauna Rescue of South Australia Inc.: http://www.faunarescue.org.au/

CPSIA information can be obtained
at www.ICGtesting.com
Printed in the USA
LVOW06s0738220617

538939LV00020B/111/P